SCHOOL
LIBRARY
SERVICE

CRUSTACEANS

by
Joanna Brundle

©2019
BookLife Publishing Ltd.
King's Lynn
Norfolk PE30 4LS

All rights reserved.
Printed in Malaysia.

A catalogue record for this book is available from the British Library.

ISBN: 978-1-78637-596-4

Written by:
Joanna Brundle

Edited by:
Emilie Dufresne

Designed by:
Gareth Liddington

PHOTOCREDITS

CONTENTS

Words that look like this are
explained in the glossary on page 31.

THE ANIMAL
KINGDOM

The animal kingdom is estimated to include over eight million known living <u>species</u>. They come in many different shapes and sizes, they each do weird and wonderful things and they live in every corner of our planet. From the freezing waters of the Arctic to the hottest deserts in the world, animals have <u>adapted</u> to diverse and often extreme conditions on Earth.

Thousands of **new** animal species are discovered **every year.**

Although every species of animal is <u>unique</u>, they share certain characteristics with each other. These shared characteristics are used to classify – or group – animals. Animals are divided into vertebrates (animals that have a backbone) and invertebrates (animals that do not have a backbone). Vertebrates include mammals, reptiles, amphibians, fish and birds. Invertebrates include a large group – or phylum – of animals called arthropods. Crustaceans are part of the arthropod phylum.

It is estimated that **over 90%** of animals are **invertebrates.**

Crustaceans include crabs, lobsters, shrimps, prawns, crayfish, sand hoppers, freshwater shrimps, water fleas, barnacles, woodlice and fish lice.

Caribbean Spiny Lobster

CRUSTACEANS

WHAT ARE CRUSTACEANS?

Crustaceans are some of the most successful animals on Earth. Fossils show that they have been around for over 540 million years.

It is estimated that there are now over 450,000 species of known crustacean. New species are constantly being discovered, especially in places that have only recently been explored, such as deep oceans. Although most crustaceans live in saltwater, some live in rivers and other freshwater habitats. Others, such as land crabs and woodlice, are terrestrial (live on land). Some species are parasites, living on the bodies of whales and fish.

Coconut Crab

Some land crabs, such as the coconut crab, are able to climb trees.

Woodlice are the only crustaceans that live entirely on land, under logs or stones.

Crustaceans are cold-blooded. This means that they cannot control their body temperature, which changes with the temperature of their environment. The body of a crustacean is made up of a number of sections called somites, to which pairs of limbs, called appendages, may be attached. These have specialist uses. They may be used for walking, grooming or mating. They may even end in claws used for fighting or holding prey. Crustaceans hatch from eggs that are usually laid in water or carried on the female's body.

The Japanese spider crab is the world's largest crustacean — it weighs up to 20 kilograms (kg) and has a leg span of up to four metres (m).

CRUSTACEAN CHECKLIST

- 🐾 Invertebrate
- 🐾 Cold-blooded
- 🐾 Most species live in water, breathing through gills
- 🐾 Lay eggs

BODY PARTS

The human skeleton is inside the body and is covered with skin and muscles, but crustaceans have an exoskeleton. This is a hard, outer layer that supports and protects them from the outside, rather than the inside. The exoskeleton is made of a tough material called chitin and is made up of separate plates, joined together by thin structures called membranes.

Freshwater Shrimp

The exoskeleton helps to protect crustaceans from being crushed or eaten by predators. The exoskeleton cannot grow bigger so, as a crustacean grows, it sheds its old exoskeleton and produces a new, larger one. This process is called moulting.

This woodlouse has just moulted.

8

Before moulting takes place, the layer under the exoskeleton, called the epidermis, produces a new exoskeleton. When this is completely formed, the old exoskeleton splits in particular, weak areas. The crustacean then pulls out of it, leaving it intact apart from the split. The new, soft exoskeleton then slowly hardens.

Can you see where the old exoskeleton of this shrimp has split?

Antennae

Crustaceans come in many forms but are made up of a head, thorax and abdomen. The head and thorax may be joined together. The head carries pairs of appendages, called antennae. These help crustaceans to sense their environment and to feed.

The legs of a crustacean are attached to the thorax and may be used for walking or swimming. The abdomen has special appendages called swimmerets that are used for swimming. At the end of the abdomen is a fan-shaped tail called the telson. Like fish, crustaceans have gills that allow them to breathe underwater. The gills are found where the legs join the thorax. Woodlice also breathe through gills.

Head

Abdomen

Claws

Antennae

Legs

Thorax

Telson

Although most crustaceans have two claws the same size, the male fiddler crab has one that is much larger than the other.

Crustaceans have a simple digestive system, or gut, which includes glands for getting rid of waste. The gut of some species, such as crabs and lobsters, has a special part called a gastric mill, which grinds up larger food particles. Like flies and other insects, crustaceans have compound eyes. Each eye is made up of many separate tube-shaped units, each of which gives a separate image, rather like a mosaic or the pieces of a jigsaw puzzle. Compound eyes allow crustaceans to pick up fast movements. This helps them to escape danger and to catch prey.

Any crustacean is able to grow a new leg or claw if one is lost, for example in fighting or escaping from an enemy. This is called autotomy. A new appendage is grown inside the exoskeleton and will appear during the next moult. It may take two or more moults before the appendage has fully grown back.

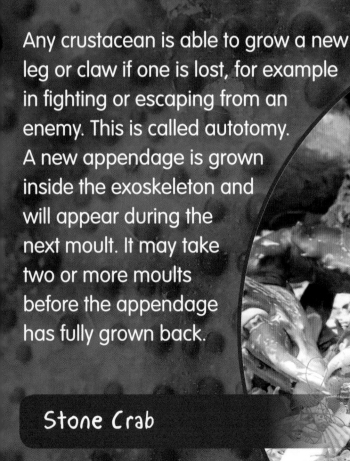

Stone Crab

GETTING AROUND

Crustaceans move around by walking, swimming, running and even jumping. Their separate body segments and jointed limbs help them to move easily. Lobsters walk slowly across the sea bed but, if they have to flee from danger, they are able to swim backwards quickly, by flipping their tails. The sandhopper is able to jump up to 40 centimetres (cm) high and up to one metre forwards, to move about or to escape predators. It does so by tucking in its tail and then rapidly flicking it out. Sandhoppers are also good swimmers.

Like many crustaceans, sandhoppers are nocturnal — feeding at night on dead seaweed and other plant material.

Although some crabs can move forwards and backwards, most move by scuttling sideways. Humans walk forwards because their knees are hinges that bend forwards. Crabs have leg joints that bend outwards, so the easiest way for them to move is in a sideways direction.

The blue swimmer crab, has one pair of legs that are flat paddles for swimming.

Adult barnacles are not able to move at all. They lay eggs that hatch into <u>larvae</u>, which drift freely in sea water. They then attach themselves to hard surfaces like rocks or harbour walls, where they feed and reproduce.

Barnacles Attached to Rocks

PREDATORS AND PREY

All animals can be sorted into groups depending on what they eat. The three main groups are carnivores, herbivores and omnivores.

Crustaceans may be carnivores, herbivores or omnivores. Some, such as crabs, lobsters and woodlice, are also classed as detrivores, feeding on dead plant and animal material.

Herbivores
Plant-Eaters

Carnivores
Meat-Eaters

Omnivores
Plant and Meat-Eaters

Crabs and lobsters are active predators, using their claws to grab prey such as fish and squid and to break open clams and mussels. As the tide comes in to cover them, barnacles feed by wafting their feathery feeding appendages, called cirri, through the water to collect plankton.

Mangrove crabs live in tropical mangrove forests, feeding on dead plants as well as other crustaceans and small fish.

Crustaceans have many predators. They form part of the diet of seals and otters as well as crocodiles and young alligators. Raccoons, apes and monkeys will wade through water to catch them. Birds are also important crustacean predators. Long-legged wading birds push their bills through water, mud and sand to find them. Gulls pick up crabs stranded on the shoreline and smash them against rocks to break their shells.

Crabs are also eaten by jellyfish, eels, turtles and octopuses.

Humans are major predators of lobsters, crabs, prawns, shrimps and crayfish. Seafood is an important <u>export</u> from many countries including Canada, India and Vietnam.

Baleen whales, which include gray and humpback whales, feed entirely on tiny crustaceans called krill, which they strain through plates in their mouths.

OCEANS, RIVERS AND LAND

Crustaceans are found in every type of saltwater and freshwater habitat. They have colonised lakes and rivers throughout the world, including even mountain lakes as high as 5,000 m above sea level. Some live in the world's deepest oceans. Some freshwater species such as fairy shrimps and tadpole shrimps live in pools that are dry for most of the year. Land-living species such as woodlice and terrestrial crabs live on every continent except Antarctica. Some crustaceans are parasites – they live on, or even inside, the bodies of other animals.

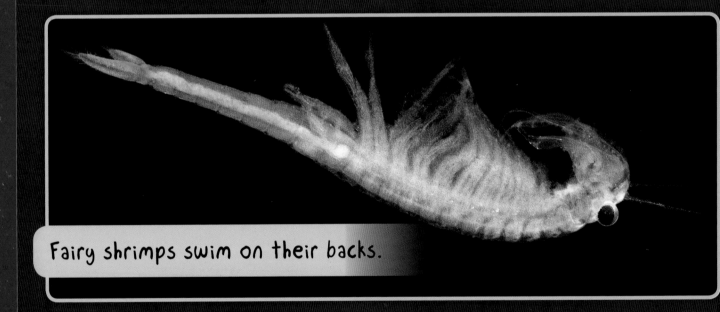

Fairy shrimps swim on their backs.

With a depth of over 11 kilometres (km), the Mariana Trench in the western Pacific Ocean is the deepest place on Earth. It is home to some species of crab and shrimp.

Sand crabs live in shifting sand in the swash zone – an area where waves are breaking onto the shore. As the tide comes in and out, the swash zone moves up and down the beach. Sand crabs move with it, burrowing backwards into wet sand. Here, they use their feathery antennae to sieve the seawater for food.

Sand Crab

Hermit crabs live in the empty shells of creatures such as whelks. As the hermit crab grows, it becomes too large for its borrowed home. It has to move out and find a new, larger home.

Some species of hermit crab live partly on land. They set up home in broken coconut shells or bamboo stems.

Hermit crabs have no hard, outer shell of their own.

ADAPTATION

Adaptations are gradual changes in the body or behaviour of an animal that help a species to survive in its habitat or to ward off predators. Crustacean appendages have been adapted for many uses. For example, the rear appendages of sand crabs have adapted into claw shapes that are great for rapid digging. Fish lice have developed a pair of disc-like suckers on their underside that they use to stick themselves firmly to the fish on which they feed.

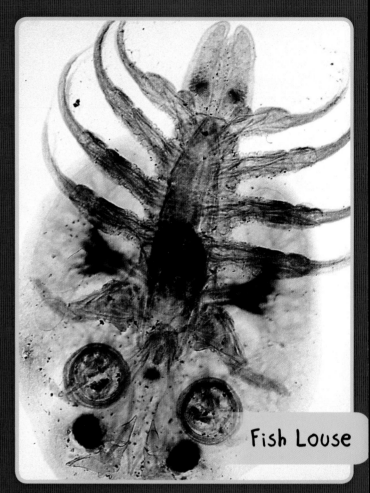

Fish Louse

Some crustaceans, such as this ghost crab, have developed eyes on stalks that help them to see all around them.

18

Crustaceans have many types of <u>camouflage</u>. Decorator crabs coat themselves in natural materials from their environment in order to hide from predators.

The colour of the shells of mud and sand crabs helps them to blend into their surroundings.

Fairy and tadpole shrimps are adapted to survive in hot, dry conditions. Although they die when their pools dry out, the eggs they have laid can survive heat, cold and drying. When the pools refill in the wet season, not all the eggs hatch at once. Some do not hatch for many years. This means that even if the pool dries again before the adults have mated, life continues whenever it refills.

This decorator crab has camouflaged itself using <u>sponges</u> and <u>algae</u>.

LIFE CYCLES

The life cycle of an animal is the series of changes that it goes through from the start to the end of its life.

Most species of crustacean have separate males and females and reproduce with a mate of the opposite sex. The female produces eggs and the male <u>fertilises</u> them. Some species release fertilised eggs directly into water. Some females carry the eggs in special appendages on their abdomen. The appendages release a sticky fluid that flows over the eggs. This attaches them firmly to the body of the female so that they are not washed away.

The female crab carries fertilised eggs in a spongy mass attached to small appendages called pleopods.

Some crustaceans show interesting mating behaviour. When a male crab finds a suitable female partner, he performs a mating 'dance'. He stands on the tips of his legs, waves his claws in the air and moves from side to side.

The eggs of most crustaceans hatch into free-swimming larvae. The larvae moult many times and grow extra appendages and body segments as they do so. The juvenile stage is the final stage before maturity, when the crustacean begins to look like a tiny adult. After more moults, adulthood is reached.

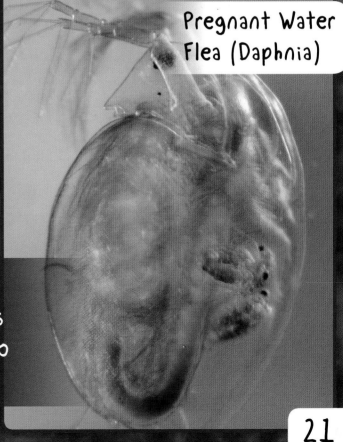

Pregnant Water Flea (Daphnia)

The eggs of water fleas and some freshwater crabs and crayfish miss out the larval stage and hatch into young that look like tiny adults.

LIFE CYCLE OF A LOBSTER

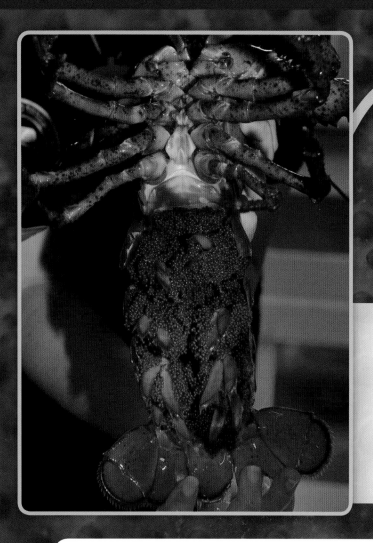

When the eggs hatch, she releases them into the water by fanning her swimmerets.

An egg-bearing lobster is also known as a 'berried' lobster – can you see why?

The female lobster mates when she has a soft shell, immediately after moulting. She produces thousands of eggs, which are carried on her tail. The female has a wider tail than the male, for this purpose.

Lobsters reach adulthood after 5 to 8 years. Moulting then slows to around once a year, then once every few years. Adults can grow to around a metre in length and, if they escape predators, can live up to 100 years.

The young larvae float near the surface, swimming and drifting in the ocean currents. At this stage, they are very likely to be eaten by fish or sea birds.

The larvae moult several times, growing appendages and body segments.

At the end of the larval stages, the few that survive settle on the floor of the ocean. They hide away from predators among <u>aquatic</u> plants or in tiny gaps between rocks. At this juvenile stage, they look like small adults, but are weaker and smaller. Lobsters moult around 25 times before reaching adulthood.

EXTREME
CRUSTACEANS

Mantis shrimps are super shrimps: super-fast and super-strong. There are over 400 species of mantis shrimp, living all around the world in shallow, tropical seas. Although only around 10 cm long, they are, relative to their size, one of the strongest animals in the world. Mantis shrimps have teardrop-shaped, club-like appendages that they use to punch their prey. The punch travels at around 80 kilometres per hour (kph) with the force of a shotgun bullet. Scientists studying mantis shrimps have to keep them in tough plastic tanks as their punch can shatter glass!

Peacock Mantis Shrimp

The punch is so fast that it produces a super-heated bubble of air. Even if the club misses its target, the heat and the force of the bubble collapsing will stun or even kill the mantis shrimp's prey. The hammer-like club can easily smash the shells of crabs, snails and rock oysters. Some species have a spear which they use with strength and speed to stab fish. Mantis shrimps also have excellent eyesight, with eyes on stalks that can move in all directions.

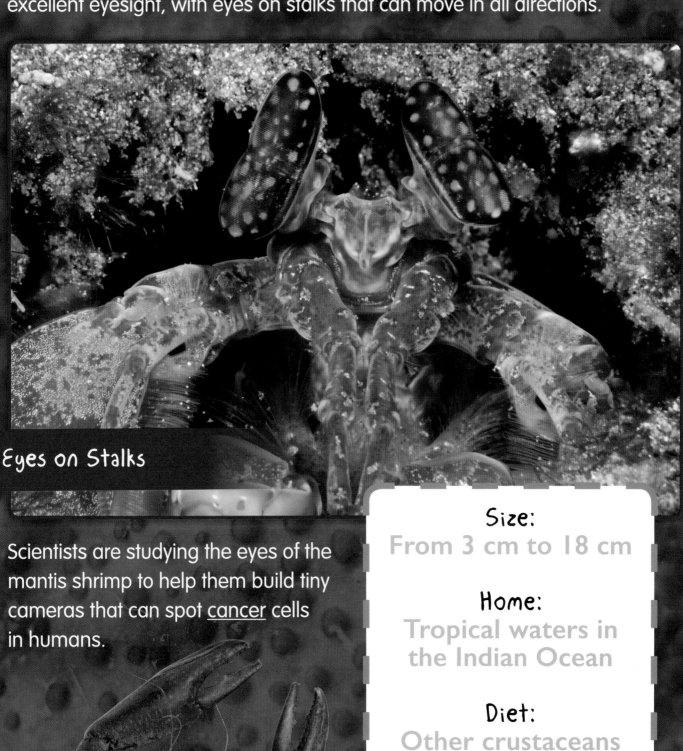

Eyes on Stalks

Scientists are studying the eyes of the mantis shrimp to help them build tiny cameras that can spot <u>cancer</u> cells in humans.

Size:
From 3 cm to 18 cm

Home:
Tropical waters in the Indian Ocean

Diet:
Other crustaceans and molluscs

Pink hairy squat lobsters are remarkable. What they lack in size — they are typically just one cm long — they more than make up for in their colour. They have bright pink bodies and legs with purple spots and are covered in white or bright yellow hairs. They are found in most tropical oceans on coral and rocky reefs, often on the underside of giant sea sponges.

Pink Hairy Squat Lobster

The skeleton shrimp's name comes from its <u>transparent</u>, stick-like body, which helps it to blend into its surroundings. Some species are even able to camouflage themselves by changing their colour. The female of some species kills the male immediately after mating, by injecting him with venom from a poisonous claw. Ouch!

Skeleton Shrimp

Size:
Up to 4 cm long

Home:
Coastal areas across the world

Diet:
Dead animal and plant material

Tasmanian giant freshwater crayfish are the world's largest freshwater invertebrates. They live in dark, slow-moving water in the rivers and streams of northern Tasmania, the only place on Earth they are found. These crayfish can live for 60 years and can grow to the size of a medium dog. Their claws are powerful enough to break human bones!

Size:
Can reach lengths of over 80 cm

Home:
Freshwater rivers in Tasmania

Diet:
Small fish and plant material

Tasmanian Giant Freshwater Crayfish

Tiny pea crabs are parasitic crustaceans. Females are a maximum of 13 millimetres (mm) long, while the males are just six mm long. They live inside the bodies of clams, oysters, mussels and other creatures, feeding on some of the food taken in by the <u>host</u>. The shell of the host protects the pea crab from predators.

Pea Crab

CRUSTACEANS UNDER THREAT

Some species of crustacean are under threat of <u>extinction</u>. Scientists estimate, for example, that a third of the world's species of crayfish face this danger. Crustaceans are an important link in the <u>food chain</u>. The most serious threats — <u>pollution</u> and global warming — are caused by the activities of humans.

POLLUTION

An estimated eight million tonnes of plastic waste, in the form of bottles, packaging and man-made fabrics, enters our oceans every year. Tiny plastic fibres have even been found in the muscles and stomachs of crustaceans living in the deepest oceans, including the Mariana Trench (see page 16).

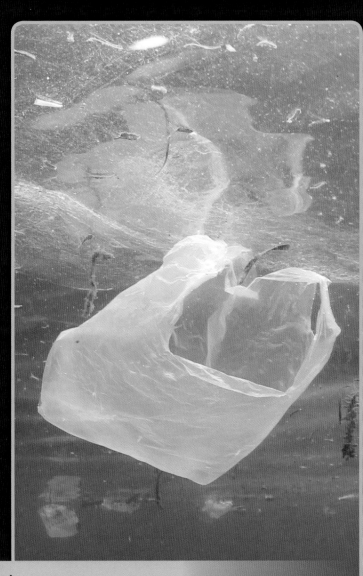

Spilled oil and human and animal waste in our oceans damages food chains by, for example, blocking natural sunlight.

It is estimated that the world's oceans contain 300 million tonnes of plastic, with five trillion pieces, weighing more than 250,000 tonnes, floating on the surface.

28

Global warming is the gradual heating up of the Earth and its oceans. The burning of <u>fossil fuels</u> releases a gas called carbon dioxide. This gas traps heat from the Earth and stops it from escaping back into space. Warming of the oceans damages coral reefs, which are a natural habitat for a quarter of all marine species, including crabs, lobsters and shrimps. Algae live inside the corals and give them their bright colours. Rising temperatures make the corals expel the algae in a process called bleaching, which eventually kills them.

Living Corals

Around a third of the carbon dioxide produced by human activities dissolves into oceans, lakes and rivers. This makes the water a more difficult environment for aquatic creatures, including crustaceans, to live in.

Bleached, Dead Corals

FIND OUT MORE

BOOKS

ANIMAL CLASSIFICATION

Discover and Learn by Steffi Cavell-Clarke

(Booklife 2017)

WEBSITES

BBC NATURE

www.bbc.co.uk/nature

Search under 'crustaceans' for news stories and clips from BBC nature programmes.

NATIONAL GEOGRAPHIC

www.nationalgeographic.com

Search under 'crustaceans' for fascinating images, videos and news stories

MARINE CONSERVATION SOCIETY

www.mcsuk.org

Search under 'crustaceans' for information about some of the threats facing marine crustaceans.

GLOSSARY

adapted	changed over time to suit an environment
algae	simple planet-like living things that have no flowers, roots, stems or leaves
aquatic	living or growing near to or in water
camouflage	traits that allow an animal to hide itself in its habitat by blending into its surroundings
cancer	a serious disease
export	to send something to another country to sell it
extinction	the process of being completely wiped out so that no living members of a species remain
fertilises	makes an egg able to develop into a new individual
food chain	a chain in which living things rely on the previous organism in the chain for food
fossil fuels	fuels, such as coal, oil and gas, that formed millions of years ago from the remains of animals and plants
fossils	the remains of prehistoric plants and animals that have been preserved in the form of stone, embedded or imprinted in rock
glands	organs in the body of an animal that secrete substances the body needs or are involved in getting rid of waste
host	an animal or plant in or on which a parasite lives
larvae	the young form of most invertebrates, amphibians and fish that hatch from eggs but undergo many changes before looking like adults
parasites	organisms that live in or on the bodies of other organisms and take their food from these other organisms
plankton	small and microscopic organisms, including small crustaceans, that drift or float in the sea or in freshwater habitats
pollution	the act of introducing to the environment a substance that is harmful or poisonous
species	a group of very similar animals that are capable of producing young together
sponges	simple invertebrate animals that draw in seawater to obtain oxygen and food
transparent	able to let light through, see-through
unique	unlike anything else

INDEX